Skateboard S

Story written by Cynthia Rider
Illustrated by Tim Archbold

Speed Sounds

Consonants

Ask children to say the sounds.

f ff	l **ll**	m	n nn	r	s ss	v ve	z zz s	sh	**th**	ng nk

b bb	c k **ck**	d	g gg	h	j	p	qu	t tt	w wh	x	y	**ch** tch

Each box contains one sound but sometimes more than one grapheme.
Focus graphemes for this story are ***circled****.*

Vowels

Ask children to say the sounds in and out of order.

a	e	i	o	u
at	h**e**n	**i**n	**o**n	**u**p

ay	ee	igh	ow	oo
d**ay**	s**ee**	h**igh**	bl**ow**	z**oo**

Story Green Words

Ask children to read the words first in Fred Talk and then say the word.

Sid Ben kid champ flip spin ramp

pest trick best trap fast past

Ask children to read the root first and then the whole word with the suffix.

stamp → stamps spot → spots

zig-zag → zig-zags sulk → sulks set → sets

Red Words

Ask children to practise reading the words across the rows, down the columns and in and out of order clearly and quickly.

the	I	he
be	says*	skateboard*
said	you	do
my	are	your

** Red Word in this book only*

Skateboard Sid

Introduction

Sid is a cool skateboard champ who can do lots of tricks on his skateboard. He's going to take part in a competition to show that he's the best. But Ben is jealous of Sid and sets a trap to try to stop him winning.

Will Sid still manage to be the champ or will Ben's plan succeed? Let's find out.

Sid, the skateboard kid,

is a champ.

He can zip and flip and spin up a ramp.

Ben says, “Skateboard Sid is a pest.”
He says, “I will trick him.
Then I will
be best.”

Ben sets his trap.
Sid zips up fast.

Sid spots Ben's
trap and
zig-zags past!

Ben sulks and sulks.

He stamps and stamps.

But Skateboard Sid is
the skateboard champ.

Questions to talk about

Ask children to TTYP for each question using 'Fastest finger' (FF) or 'Have a think' (HaT).

p.9	(FF)	What can Sid do on a skateboard?
p.10	(FF)	What does Ben think of Sid? What does he decide to do?
p.11	(FF)	What does Sid do when he spots the trap?
p.12	(HaT)	How does Ben feel about Sid zig-zagging past the trap? (frustrated, furious, grumpy)